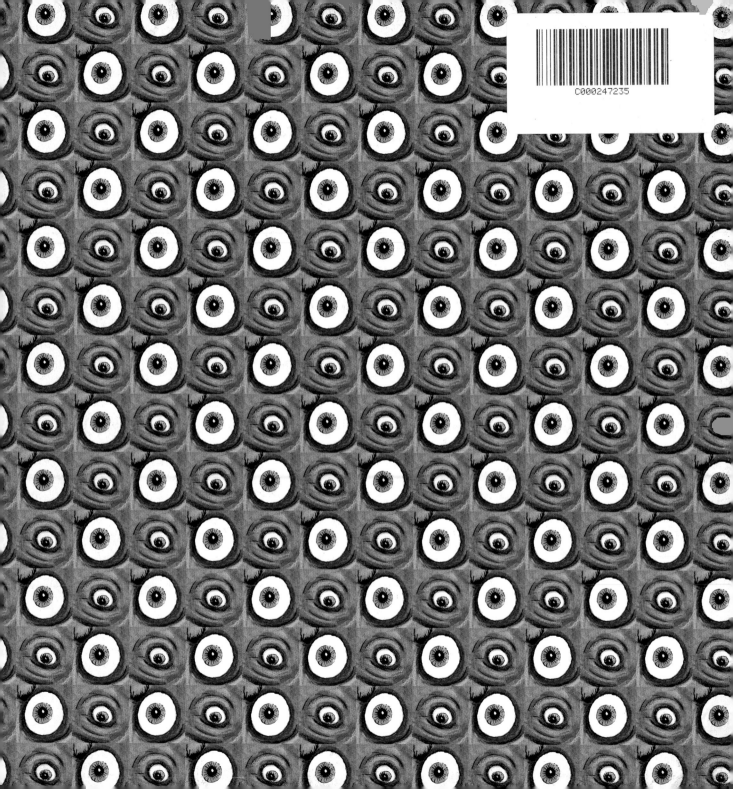

C000247235

MY VISION
FOR A
NEW YOU

For Pat and Jim, wherever they are.

Also by Steve Bell

Unspeakable If...
Unstoppable If...
Bell's Eye: Twenty Years of Drawing Blood
If... Bottoms Out
The If... Files
Apes of Wrath
If… Marches On

by Steve Bell and Brian Homer

Chairman Blair's Little Red Book

MY VISION
FOR A **NEW YOU**

methuen

in association with

1 3 5 7 9 10 8 6 4 2

First published in 2006 by Methuen in association with The Guardian

Copyright in the cartoons © 1990, 1991, 1993, 1994, 1995, 1996, 1997, 1998, 1999, 2000, 2001, 2002, 2003, 2004, 2005, 2006 by Steve Bell
Copyright in the text © 2006 by Steve Bell

The right of Steve Bell to be identified as author of this work has been asserted by him in accordance with the Copyright, Designs and Patents Act 1988

A CIP catalogue record for this book is available from the British Library

ISBN 10: 0-413-77593-3
ISBN 13: 978-0-413-77593-1

Methuen Publishing Ltd
11–12 Buckingham Gate, London SW1E 6LB
Methuen Publishing Limited Reg. No. 3543167
www.methuen.co.uk

This book is published in association with Guardian Books. Guardian Books is an imprint of Guardian Newspapers Limited. The Guardian is a registered trademark of Guardian Media Group plc.

Designed by Homer Creative
www.homercreative.com

Printed and bound in Great Britain by CPI/Bath Press

Contents

How to use this book 3

1	Let's Talk About You	4
2	Who Are You?	10
3	Thinking About You	16
4	The Giving Age	25
5	Know Your Enemies	28
6	Know Your Friends	33
7	The Will To Power	40
8	The Power Of Language	44
9	The Big Picture	48
10	Achieve That Vision	53
11	Speak Your Truth	77
12	The Space–Time Continuum	85
13	Good Faith	88
14	Seize The Future	91
15	My Task	97
16	Acting Boldly	100
17	A Bird For The Bush	105
18	My Little Blue Pill	110
19	Image And Substance	119
20	Gordon Has Substance	122
21	Blatcherism – The Real Thing	126
22	Make Your Play	132
23	Queen Lear	138
24	This Silly Game	143
25	Learn Your Lessons	144
26	Successful Centre Ground Politics	150
27	Get Out Of The Bathroom	152
28	The British People	154

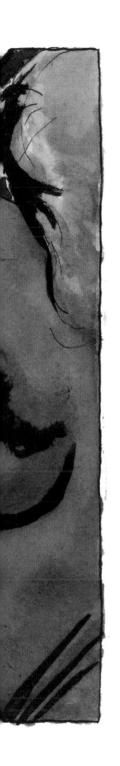

How to use this book

This book tells a story, but it also operates on a subliminal level.

My vision, in the form of my look, appears on almost every page.

By the time you have finished reading it you may well start seeing my look, even when it isn't necessarily there. This is a quite harmless function of my Whole New Vision for a New You, and will not influence your perception of everyday objects at all. It may however be inadvisable to operate machinery immediately after putting down this volume.

CHAPTER 1

Let's Talk About You

You've bought this book, which means that you have taken the first step on the road that will lead to a whole new person, and that new person . . . is you!

Think about that for a minute.

This book isn't trying to sell you something you don't want or don't need; it's not trying to tell you what to do, how to live or what to be. Those are all yesterday's prescriptions and yesterday's thinking.

What this book is going to do is something far simpler and far more relevant.

It is going to give you back to yourself, and that is something quite remarkable.

- © Steve Bell 2000 ~ 10·9·00· AFTER REMBRANDT -

6

Your Irreducible Core

Every individual has something that is unique to them, what might be called their irreducible core, something that is very special and very precious. Yet how many of us are dissatisfied with what we actually are?

How many of us feel on the margins, left behind, outside the envelope of existence?

Worse still, how many of us actually want to be somebody else?

What could be sadder than that?

What Happens In Life

Some people achieve success, some people don't: that's what happens in life and it's neither a good thing nor a bad thing.

This book is not going to give you a route map to success. No book could do that and if it said it could it would be lying.

What a book can do, however, is to set forth some very clear and simple principles, and if these principles are understood and taken to heart and then acted upon – well, maybe then, who knows? Anything is possible. Success, celebrity, even happiness, but that's not for the book to say.

The question is: what do you want?

And before you can answer that you have to know this one simple thing: who are you?

After GILLRAY –

LIGHT *expelling Darkness* — *Evaporation of Stygian Exhalations* — or — The SUN of the CONSTITUTION *rising superior to the Clouds of OPPOSITION.*

CHAPTER 2

Who Are You?

These are the questions that have to be asked before we can begin our journey together, which is what this book intends to be, so, since I would not dream of telling you what to think, I will start by giving you my own answers to those questions.

11

Who Am I?

My name is Tony Blair. Easy for you to say, I hear you declare, but no less true for that. I am Tony Blair. I'm a fairly straight kind of guy. People know my face, some of them may even have voted for me. I've been around for quite a while now. I hope to be around for a lot longer. That much is obvious. I've had success, I've been at the top for a good few years, and there is one thing I'm fairly certain of that might be less obvious, and it is this: I've got nothing left to prove so my advice to you is sound.

Where Should I Go?

Where do you go next when you've reached the top?

Is it up? That by definition would be impossible, or I'd have to go to Mars. Is it down? Sometimes it's tempting to think in terms of what goes up must come down, but for me, down is not a place I want to be. It's not an option.

Is it sideways? The logic of gravity tells us that sideways is where Wiley Coyote goes when he hurtles off a cliff in pursuit of the Road Runner. There is a moment of purest fantasy while he hangs in the air, and then it's down all over again. Bugger sideways, as my erstwhile spiritual adviser John Prescott used to say.

So where does that leave us? Everywhere and nowhere? No way. There's another way, here, now, at the intersection between old and new, with Tony Blair, into the future.

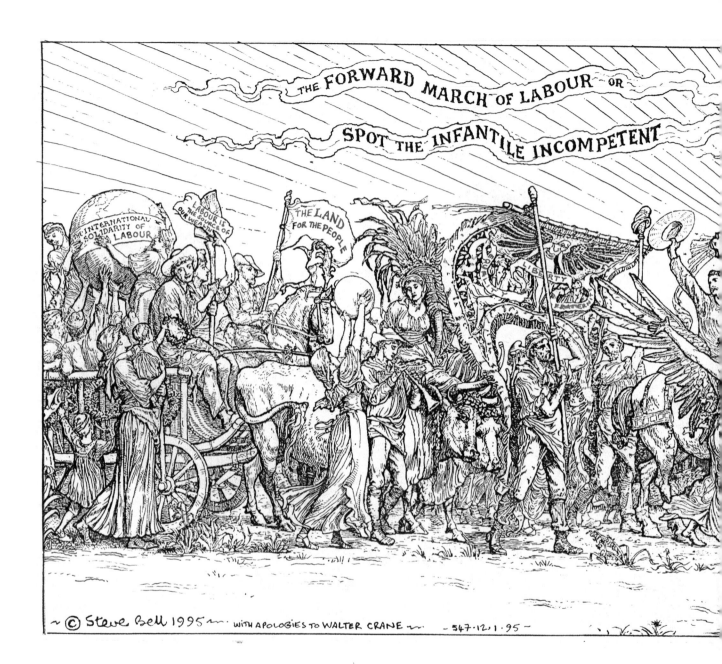

What Do I Want?

Put simply, I want success for the British People. Let's be clear, I cannot give them success. Only God can do that. But if we can become a nation that is more at ease with itself, more in tune with its own true values, with its irreducible core, then success will surely follow, as day follows night. I want to put Britain more at ease with itself and, as any therapist now working will tell you, there are techniques for this sort of thing.

CHAPTER 3

Thinking About You

So now let's think about you. Bear in mind the lessons you've learned in the previous pages.

17

Ask The British People

When the Labour Party was beaten for the fourth time in a row in 1992, I decided to go out and ask the British people what it was that they really wanted for themselves and for their families. It wasn't rocket science. They didn't want impossible dreams. They wanted to better themselves. There was a man, quite a young man, polishing his Sierra, and I'm grateful to that young man because what he told me changed my life.

'You lot, you're not interested in people like me. I just want to get on in life, to get a better house, a better car, a blow job on the side, maybe even a lobster thermidor on the wife's birthday, but all you ever want to do is take my money and dole it out to work-shy foreigners. Why don't you fuck off and die and take your gleaming teeth with you!?'

Sierra Man

Who Do You Think You Are?

Who does Mick Jagger think he is? He thinks he's Mick Jagger, a rock star. How does he know that? Because he's had it confirmed by various independent sources, most notably his friends and his family, and of course the fellow members of his rock band. Also, at the end of the day he can look at his bank balance and listen to his fans.

You're not Mick Jagger so you can't do any of that, and if you did try you'd probably be arrested.

You're Not Tony Blair

So who are you? You're not Tony Blair, I can tell you that for nothing, or at least for the price of this book, and if you think you're me you've got problems. I, on the other hand, know that I am Tony Blair, not simply for similar reasons to Mick Jagger, but because I, unlike Mick Jagger, was put where I am, indeed made what I am today by none other than the British people, in other words by you, so I know where you're coming from.

What Makes You Think?

Nobody is interested in politics, but everybody likes moaning about politicians. Why should this be?

Is it because we're all useless and evil? Or is it because, as someone once pointed out, politics is like show business for ugly people? Are we as ugly and useless and evil as people seem to believe? I think not, and I'm not just saying that because of who I am.

I think it's simply because we're the ones in charge, and you don't like anyone being in charge of you because you're either a feckless baby boomer, the descendant of a feckless baby boomer, or you're a clapped-out old wreck on the fast track to the grave.

Whichever it is, you don't really appreciate the bigger picture.

CHAPTER 4

The Giving Age

On May 2 1997, the Giving Age began. At last the British people had a government that embodied their own truest values, but it didn't happen by accident, and it wouldn't have happened if I had not done the groundwork, and that had begun a long, long time before.

A Toss About You

When I first went up to Oxford back in the 1970s I knew that I wanted to go into politics, but frankly I didn't know which party to go for. Being from a fairly non-political family that, to be honest, was neither rich nor poor, the old class-based politics of labour versus capital had no particular appeal to me one way or the other. The Liberals on the other hand struck me as a party of vague compromise without the faintest hope of achieving power – and what is politics, after all, without power, except hopeless vanity?

So I took a coin, flipped it, called heads for Labour, tails for Conservative, and if it landed on its side I would join the Liberals.

It came up heads.

CHAPTER 5

Know Your Enemies

In politics, as in other aspects of life, it is necessary to know who your friends are and to be able to identify your enemies.

As Margaret Thatcher discovered to her cost in 1990, your real enemies are usually behind you.

That is one lesson I took very much to heart before I ever became leader of the Labour Party.

127.29.10.90

~ THE GOLDEN SCENARIO ~ ~ ©Steve Bell 1990 ~

29

Socialism Is Evil

The other, more positive lesson I took from Margaret Thatcher was that, quite simply, socialism is evil.

Saying socialism is one thing. We all did that back in the sixties, seventies and into the eighties, it was the fashion, like long hair and flared trousers.

Doing socialism is something else entirely.

Look at its track record: National Socialism ruined Germany, devastated Europe and led directly to the deaths of tens of millions of people; Soviet Socialism ruined Russia and China (until they abandoned it), devastated vast tracts of Europe and Asia and led directly to the deaths of even more millions.

That's why Scargill had to go and that's why I got rid of him and his ilk within months of becoming leader, and that's why, when Margaret Thatcher defeated Scargill in 1985, it was for the good of humanity rather than the destruction of community.

CHAPTER 6

Know Your Friends

While it may be surprising to hear me say I hate socialism, people may be even more shocked when I say that I love Gordon Brown. Can you imagine Tony without Gordon? I think not. But then why do some seem to think that they can have Gordon without Tony? Surely that would be equally unthinkable, and certainly no way to help the British people achieve the success they crave.

You may find this hard to believe, but I love Gordon Brown with a passion bordering on the physically inappropriate. I freely admit that I would never have got where I am today without him. Gordon is my anchor, my rock, my bottom. Without Gordon I would be a lightweight, albeit a handsome and intelligent one.

That's why talk of splits, jealousies, resentments and relationship breakdowns is so misplaced. I love Gordon Brown, but sadly Gordon has a problem loving me. He's a man who tends to shrink from the honest expression of emotion, and so has difficulty in acknowledging the immense affection he has borne me for a very long time. Politically, he is my other half and I am his. Emotionally, it is just the same.

Learning To Love

For once the problem is not something manufactured by a sensation-hungry media.

The real reason lies with our other other halves, so to speak. There was a time when Cherie and Sarah hated each other like poison, and Cherie hated Gordon just as much as Sarah detested Tony.

But you know what? They don't anymore, because of one powerful, overriding factor which can benefit you too: my Vision.

Now they are like two sisters, while Gordon and I are like a same-sex couple, high-powered, self-motivated, independent and at last pulling in the same direction.

Renewing Your Values

The first time Cherie and I took a Mexican Shit Bath (or MSB to give it its more polite title) is not an occasion I normally care to dwell on. It was a life-changing moment, nonetheless. Lowering oneself into the giant tank of lukewarm central American excrement demands a strong will and an even stronger stomach. Abandoning oneself to the foul-smelling slurry is not something one does lightly, but I can honestly say that it was worth every moment of humiliating discomfort.

It was nothing short of a rebirth for us, for our relationship and, ultimately, for the Labour Party.

There is one guaranteed cast-iron certainty when you emerge from an MSB, and it is this:

THINGS CAN ONLY GET BETTER.

CHAPTER 7

The Will To Power

The Will to Power is not bestowed on everyone for the very simple reason that it would drive most people stark mad. Only very few have the constitutional resilience to cope with it, because we have the rare ability to see ourselves in context.

We appreciate destiny and sense direction because we understand the bigger picture.

This enables us to plan for action.

41

RAISING THE STANDARD OF INTERNATIONAL JUSTICE, MAZ

What Leadership Means

After 9/11 I knew what needed to be done before I ever even spoke to President Bush. I understood that the world had changed forever and probably not for the better. I knew there were certain things that needed to be done and so I did not hesitate in setting about getting them done.

That is what leadership means.

I am disappointed that a dogged determination to fight evil should be so fatally misconstrued as doglike devotion to the whim of an idiot.

CHAPTER 8

The Power Of Language

President George W. Bush is no idiot and people misunderestimate him at their peril. That bizarre yet simple word gives us a clue to the real workings of his mind. He is often self-deprecating about his problems with the English language, but this one word – a coining, one might say a 'Bushism' – is a mark of the purest genius.

Only a truly balanced mind in a completely open and relaxed state of heightened perception could produce such a rare fusion of sound, sense and meaning. It might invite snorts of derision from the less acute observer, but ultimately this new language enlightens us.

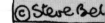

©SteveBel

1701·15·1·02 —

45

My deputy, John Prescott, has a similar gift of expression. It transcends the culture of 'spin' and is wholly genuine. Both men have distinctly regional accents which lend their pronouncements the proud stamp of authenticity. John, in his own words, is 'norra fookin dog', and George is proud of his mission to spread 'Freeman Moxy roun the wurl'.

My approach to language is very different. Where George and John are marked by regional distinction, I seek broad consensus in my vowel sounds, being neither north nor south, east nor west, high nor low, rich nor poor, left nor right. Where John might say 'werld' and George might say 'wurl', I say 'wowld'; where John says 'ealthcur', I say 'howfcar'; and where everyone else says 'benefits', I say 'bunufuts'.

This is not affectation, but simply my own voice seeking to synthesise and transcend potential barriers to communication.

It's a softer, more rounded, less confrontational approach to diction and I firmly believe that the bunufuts to mankind will be enormous.

47

CHAPTER 9

The Big Picture

In 1998 I said, in relation to the peace negotiations in Northern Ireland, that:

'This is no time for soundbites, but I feel the hand of history on my shoulder.'

I have to tell you now: I meant every single word.

Historic Action

It was never a time for mere sloganising, rather a moment for historic action. Government is about performance and I was fully conscious of the significance of that moment. It was, literally, awe-inspiring, and I freely admit to being more than a little nervous.

At times like that you can either retreat into your shell, put your head under the pillow and withdraw from the world, or you can face the music, march towards the sound of gunfire and make the future happen.

It is a question of perspective. My immediate experience was of a cold sweat, some heart palpitations and the body odour of a certain civil servant who shall, for now, remain nameless. On the next level, so to speak, I was aware of the people around me, the papers in front of me, the various parties to the conflict in the room and the reporters, photographers and TV cameramen. On the level above that I was aware of the global significance of the occasion.

Everybody can have that kind of awareness, but only very, very few can have the capability to connect with that perception and act on the third level.

It takes training, it requires aptitude – but above all it demands Vision.

CHAPTER 10

Achieve That Vision

To achieve that Vision, there are a number of key stages of perception that need to be gone through. For each stage there is a simple exercise to enable understanding and achievement of that heightened state of perceptual awareness.

This book will furnish you with all three, plus another one for luck.

STAGE ONE

Find a place where you can relax without any pressure from the outside world. You may wish to be seated or you can lie down somewhere comfortable. I would recommend closed curtains and a darkened room, but these are really unimportant details. It is important, however, that you will remain undisturbed. Some of these exercises may cause you to cry out loud and I do not wish this book to be the cause of any embarrassment. A light source, preferably a pink light-bulb or lamp of no more than 40 watts, is essential.

4.2.5.05~

WAKING UP WITH MICHAEL HOWARD ～ AFTER HOGARTH © Steve Bell 2005

RELAX Relax, close your eyes and breathe deeply. Feel all your muscles relaxing. Feel the muscles of your face relaxing. Breathe very deeply. Experience a benign sense of your own wellbeing. Nothing is going to disturb you, make demands on you or hurt you in any way. Feel the beginnings of a smile forming on your face, not a grimace, not a forced expression, simply an extension of your relaxed state. Feel your lower lip slacken. Keeping your eyes shut, feel your smile growing, expanding, affirming your positive feelings about yourself, your loved ones, your family and your pets. Imagine the sun shining on you, its warmth spreading across your face. Your breathing is steady. Your smile is growing, growing just as steadily.

STAGE TWO

Without moving your head, and while continuing to breathe deeply, slowly open your right eye. Do not focus on anything but sense the dim, pinkish glow of the lamp, suffusing the room. Let your smile guide your vision as sensations of wellbeing flood through your face and your body. Breathe deeper and deeper, then shallower and shallower. Deeper and deeper, shallower and shallower. Your smile is becoming wider and wider, your jaw looser and looser. Deeper and deeper, shallower and shallower, wider and wider, looser and looser. Continue this process while you count backwards from 300 – 299 – 298 – 297 – 296 – 295… imagine the sun's warmth permeating every fibre of your being. Feel your smile growing in an unfocussed pink haze.

STAGE THREE

Continue your breathing and smiling pattern: deeper and deeper, shallower and shallower, wider and wider, looser and looser. Think positive thoughts about your loved ones, the world, its wonders and beauties until your backward count reaches 50 – 49 – 48 – 47… now begin to think about the world's problems too, but in a positive way, imagining how you will deal with poverty, conflict, global warming, library books overdue, now feel small discomforts starting to encroach on your inner wellbeing as you continue counting down, 10 – 9 – 8 – 7 – 6 – 5 – 4 – 3 – 2 – 1 –

OPEN YOUR LEFT EYE AS WIDE AS YOU CAN.

©Steve Bell

2265 · 27 · 7 · 05

© Steve Bell 2005

BREATHE Everything is now in sharp, bright focus as you see everything more clearly, envisioning more deeply and vividly than ever before. Sit up, then stand, or stand up if you have been sitting. Look directly into the lamp. Look at the curtains if you have them, move towards them and boldly open them. Open the door if you haven't. Step outside if you can, take hungry gulps of air, breathe as deeply as you can but take quicker breaths, and quicker still until you are almost panting. Stride forth into the world and

MAKE THE FUTURE HAPPEN.

STAGE FOUR

(Stage Four is optional unless you aspire to political leadership, in which case it is essential.)

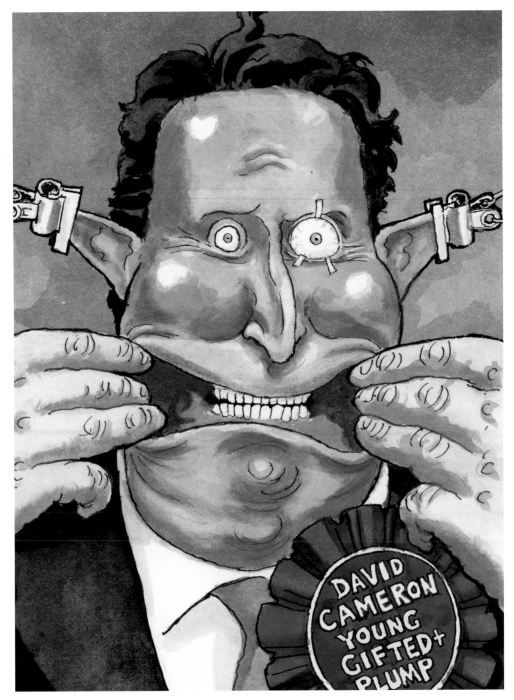

All of us have certain people or situations that cause us problems and which under normal circumstances we would seek to avoid. This fourth exercise will enable you to confront and to deal with these sources of negative energy.

HELL Contrary to what that old Marxist existentialist reprobate Jean-Paul Sartre would have had you believe, hell is not other people. Quite the contrary, when other people are dealt with in a clear, firm, honest and straightforward manner, other people can be very heaven.

I have no problem with other people because I know that, in essence, other people are just the same as me.

I would go further.

RIGOUR , REALISM and RESPONSIBILITY.
A MEDLEY.

Believe not every Spirit, but try the Spirits whether they are of God: because many false Prophets are gone out into the World.

1 John. Ch. 4. V. 1.

Design'd and Engrav'd by W.m Hogarth.   Defaced by Steve Bell © 1997   Publish'd as the Act directs March y.e 15.th 1762.

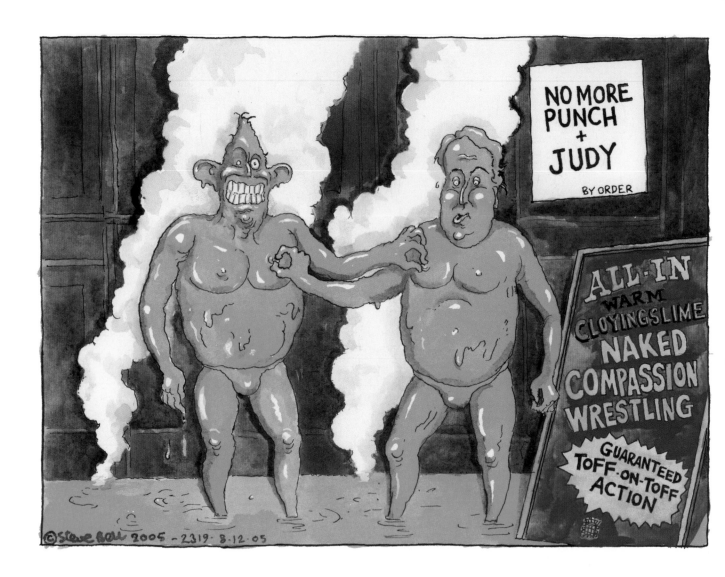

HEAVEN

OTHER PEOPLE ARE ME

68

I AM OTHER PEOPLE

BECOME

I would strongly advise anyone who wishes to become a politician, yet continues to entertain the faintest suspicion that hell is other people, to think again. If you wish to help, say, the British people, or the Norwegian people, or the Iraqi people to succeed, you must do more than merely empathise with them.

YOU MUST
BECOME
THEM AND
THEY MUST
BECOME YOU.

FOCUSSED

Stage Four is simply this: perform stages one, two and three as outlined above, but, before striding out to make the future happen while continuing to maintain the frenzied state of focussed hyperventilation, recite the following verses. It may help to commit them to memory (very minor changes have been made to obviate cultural offence):

'If you can walk with crowds and keep your virtue,
Or walk with Kings – nor lose the common touch,
If neither foes nor loving friends can hurt you,
If all men count with you, but none too much;
If you can fill the unforgiving minute
With sixty seconds worth of distance run,
Yours is the Earth and everything that's in it,
And – which is more – you'll be a real person!'

2308·16·11·05·

Now the future's yours.
MAKE IT HAPPEN!

HAVE
LUMP
EAD...

CHAPTER 11

Speak Your Truth

Only you can describe the world from your viewpoint. No-one else can replicate the unique perspective that only you have. It is unique in space, and in time, but, as everyone knows, space shifts and time changes. Maintaining your unique view of the world through shifting spaces and changing times is a challenging task, which in itself requires a reformulation of space and time and consequently a redefinition of your truth. I'll repeat that so you remember it:

REFORMULATE SPACE AND TIME.

REDEFINE YOUR TRUTH.

Seize The Moment

At this point I wish to introduce the notion of belief, and to elaborate the concept of Belief Inside the Moment.

The existentialists, led by Sartre, were very keen on living inside the moment, which is not, of itself, a bad thing. Living inside the moment in a state of heightened awareness – making the most of the present, living life to its very fullest extent or possibility – is very important and deeply worthwhile.

79

STANDING BY HIS INTELLIGENCE...

Where Sartre and Co. went wrong was in divorcing the moment from its moral context. The four existential truths – Death, Isolation, Meaninglessness and Freedom – are all very well up to a point, if a little grim. Death comes to us all without a doubt. Isolation is undeniable, given the atomised nature of our individual sparks of consciousness. Freedom is incontrovertible since we all have free will. But Meaninglessness?

This is where I take issue with the existentialists since, if every person, every thing and every occurrence is essentially meaningless, what sense does that make of the bigger picture?

82

We Are Here For A Purpose

People may have taken issue with my assertion that I am a fairly straight kind of guy, but I've never kept hidden my core beliefs and nor, to be fair, have I ever shoved them down anyone's throat.

I do however have two fundamental beliefs which for me are non-negotiable. I believe in the power of love and I believe that we are here on earth for a purpose.

As Alastair once memorably said: we don't 'do' religion. The over-demonstrative trailing of one's religious convictions is definitely not the British way. But it doesn't mean we don't have religion.

CHAPTER 12

The Space–Time Continuum

If we accept all that modern science teaches us about the space–time continuum and the mutability of all things, that nothing is constant and that all things are relative, we still cannot deny the overpowering human need for belief. By that reasoning, however, belief can only be possible inside the moment since, at the very next moment everything may change (and change it most definitely will). We can only therefore speak our truth inside the moment and, by extension, our truth can only apply to that particular moment. Thus a thing will only be true if we believe it, and will only continue to be true if we carry on believing it. A different truth may require a different belief, but it will still be true as long as it is honestly believed in. The status quo can never be an option because the only certainty is change. That is why I am a moderniser and can only ever be a moderniser.

To those who may doubt the wisdom of believing in different, possibly conflicting truths at different points in time, I can only draw their attention to the important dimension of faith.

CHAPTER 13

Good Faith

A truth that is believed in good faith, which suddenly gives way to a different, or even opposing truth, should present no moral or logical problem, providing both truths are believed in, in equal good faith, at the moment of belief. It is a truism to say that faith can move mountains, but it may be less so to point out that this is every bit as true in the moral and spiritual realm as it is in the temporal and physical.

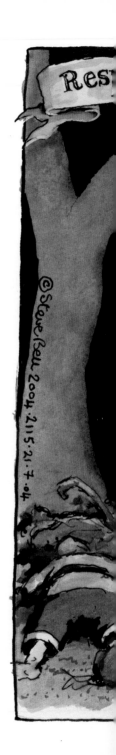

CHAPTER 14

Seize The Future

When, before the last election, I announced my intention not to stand for a fourth term in office, I sincerely believed that to be the truth. I am now honestly convinced that that particular truth no longer obtains. Indeed I now firmly believe with all the good faith I have ever mustered in my entire life that the opposite is true and that it is now absolutely essential that I stand again.

92

The House Of Power

I love Gordon Brown too much to bequeath him the apparent shambles that my third term has become. It is my duty to put my own house in order and, since my house is the house of power in this country, that is the house I must put right.

Gordon Brown simply cannot deliver the right-wing red meat that the British people crave so fervently. It is no mere accident of symbolism that Gordon is completely blind in his left eye. No matter how honest, capable and hard-working he is (and he is all this and more) he cannot supply the Vision necessary for the task in hand.

David Cameron has a similar impediment, though not in the physical sense, and Sir Menzies Campbell's Visionary acuity is so feeble as to be pretty well non-existent.

96

CHAPTER 15

My Task

Thus it is once more my task to lead my party to an historic fourth term in office. To call this unprecedented would be to belittle the significance of such a victory, and if my party should be so short-sighted as to question such a course of action, then in good faith I should have no option but to find another, more realistic and modern-minded party to share my destiny.

Rectify The Anomalies

Before that can happen, however, there are certain anomalies in the field of policy that need to be cleared up.

I intend to fight the next election on a pro-nuclear, anti-global warming, anti-war, anti-disestablishment, anti-organised crime, pro-life, pro-hanging, pro-free market and pro-land reform ticket.

CHAPTER 16

Acting Boldly

On the anti-war question, while my credentials may seem questionable, my position in reality is unassailable. Only I, in good faith, got us into the quagmire that Iraq has become, so only I am best placed to, in equal good faith, extract us from that terrible situation.

"RIDING PILLION WITH A POWERFUL ALLY HAS PROVED COSTLY IN TERMS
BRITISH AND AMERICAN MILITARY LIVES, IRAQI LIVES...AND THE DAMAG
TO THE COUNTER TERRORISM CAMPAIGN" — ROYAL INSTITUTE FOR INTERNATION

UNEASY RIDER

©Steve Bell 2005 - 2260·19·7·05

Solid, Popular Proposals

I believe it to be the root cause of my current unpopularity, and, yes, I do acknowledge that I have become unpopular. So by acting boldly and in good faith to remove that cause I can, in conjunction with the other solid, popular proposals outlined above, achieve not just an unparalleled fourth term, but a fourth consecutive landslide.

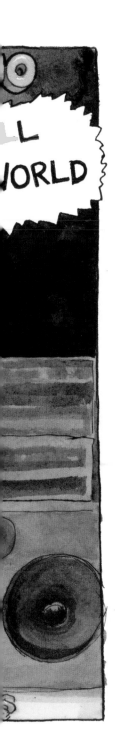

CHAPTER 17

A Bird For The Bush

Another potent factor in my historic renewal will be the removal of my good friend and ally, President George W. Bush from office, which is bound to happen before January 2009. While the President's popularity in his own country is on a par with, if not slightly higher than mine, his popularity ratings in this country are so low as to be undetectable by modern statistical methodology. This is partly, as outlined above, due to a general cultural misunderstanding of the President and his way with what we still consider to be our language.

It is also the consequence of some rather egregious untruths that he personally delivered to me, and by extension to the British people, in what I suspect may not have been the best of faith.

I've Said It Now

Was it Lao Tsu or Baden-Powell who said that in order to overcome your opponents you first have to become them? Well, I've said it now, so it may be unnecessary to point out that once you have removed someone's very right to exist, in other words their unique identity, then you have removed the principal source of their strength and can therefore destroy them utterly. Of course, in the wrong hands this technique could be appallingly dangerous, but it was precisely how I became my predecessor, Margaret Thatcher, and will yet become my putative successor, whether it be Gordon Brown, David Cameron or that funny little bloke, no, not Ming, the other one.

THE END OF THE AFFAIR

© Steve Bell 2000 – 1536·23·11·00 –

The Labour Party Must Die

Our Lord has a good deal to teach us on this subject. He died to bring us all the possibility of eternal life just as the Labour Party must die to bring me eternal leadership. And die it surely must. I mean, who's going to vote for a bureaucratic Scots tightwad with all the raw charismatic power of a large codfish on a fishmonger's slab? I wouldn't and neither will the British people.

CHAPTER 18

My Little Blue Pill

Neil Kinnock took over as leader of the Labour Party in 1983, which was, in a way, his tragedy and the party's misfortune. I was clearly not in the running at the time as I had only just been elected as an MP.

Neil was the only available candidate who seemed able to find the party's 'G' spot, so to speak. Neil was, or had been, a radical left-wing firebrand with a gift for the telling phrase. 'I warn you not to be sick, I warn you not to be old…' was one of his finest from that very time after the worst defeat in the party's history.

Electrifying Jolt

I was never quite sure what he was driving at since I for one never had any intention of becoming either sick or old. Yet, in the heat and pressure of the office of Leader of Her Majesty's Official Opposition his eloquence seemed to desert him. All his fiery rhetoric became submerged beneath qualifying clauses and the necessary, but for him rather boring language of political realism.

Under Neil the party became used to disappointment, came indeed to expect it. It lost its sense of excitement and became desensitized. After eleven years of such inept treatment in the hands of Neil Kinnock and his successor John Smith, its libido needed reawakening, and I supplied the electrifying jolt it needed to get it writhing with pleasure again.

— APOLOGIES TO RAYMOND BRIGGS —

A Really Good Seeing To

Yet now, after nine years of expert handling it is as if the party has become sated, blasé, can take no more and so, by tragic extension, is thoroughly desensitized again. To be brutal, the party seems to have suffered circumcision, clitoridectomy and full frontal lobotomy all rolled into one. The party has had a really good and expert seeing to and mistakenly thinks that all it needs now is a nice cup of tea. But it needs more than that. It needs more than rhetoric, more than charisma, more than mere electricity to get it going again.

There is no occupation

© Steve Bell 2004 · 2140·1·10·04

It needs death followed by rebirth and only I can achieve that. Indeed the death of the party has already been achieved as I myself have become the party and the party is now me.

I HAVE ALREADY DESTROYED THE LABOUR PARTY.

969-15-7-97-©Steve Bell 1997

PEOPLE'S
PANEL

I JOINED T
PEOPLE'S PA
AND ALL I C
WAS THIS
CRAPPY T-S

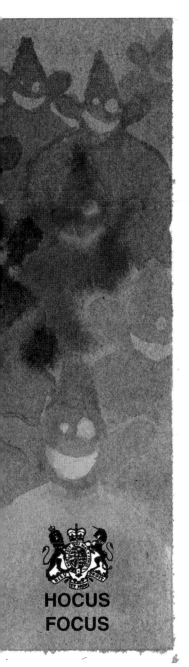

HOCUS
FOCUS

CHAPTER 19

Image And Substance

In politics, image and substance are one and the same thing.

The Appearance Of Delivery

Where the Tories go wrong is in their repeated criticisms of my government's failure to 'deliver'. In this they are barking up the wrong tree because they know and I know that what they are really calling for is not actual 'delivery' but the appearance of delivery. They couldn't tell the difference and nor, I humbly submit, could anybody. If they really wanted me to actually 'deliver' anything they would be wishing themselves out of a job.

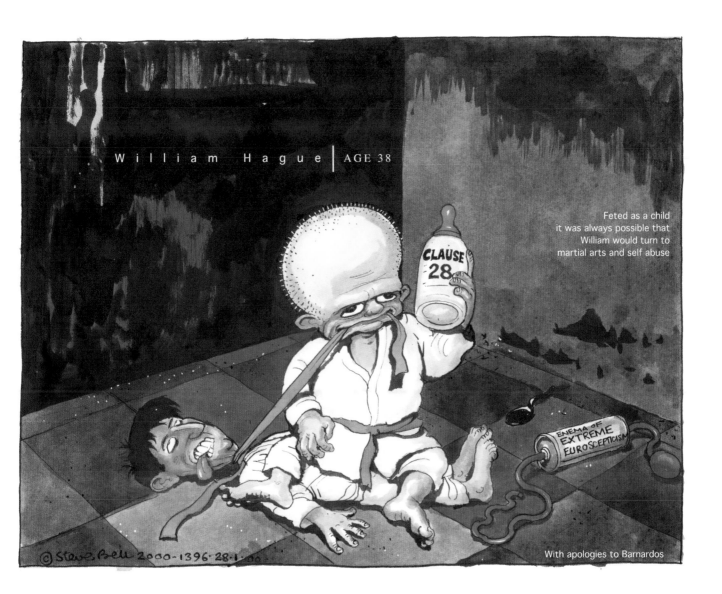

William Hague | AGE 38

Feted as a child
it was always possible that
William would turn to
martial arts and self abuse

© Steve Bell 2000-1396·28·1·00

With apologies to Barnardos

121

CHAPTER 20

Gordon Has Substance

I understand appearance in a way that they clearly do not, yet I also appreciate substance. Gordon has substance in abundance. He 'does' substance in the same way that I 'do' conviction. But it is the appearance of substance and the appearance of conviction that we do so well. The Tories as yet can do neither.

123

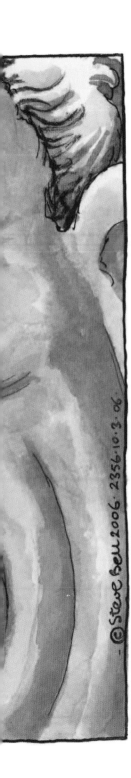

The Substance Will Evaporate

Look at the contest between Gordon and his shadow, George Osborne.

Exactly. There isn't one. Osborne barely qualifies as an excrescence.

Yet where would Gordon's substance be without my conviction? Under close scrutiny it would crumble into dust, because Gordon's substance is partly grounded in the appearance of something that it actually isn't, which is vaguely socialistic. Remove that protective illusion and the substance will evaporate.

CHAPTER 21

Blatcherism – The Real Thing

If the Tories are to succeed at anything they will have to ditch Digital Dave, who is patently incapable of supplying even the shadow of the ghost of the appearance of Blatcherism, and go for the real thing, in other words, me.

And I'm not going anywhere just yet.

© Steve Bell 2004 · 2116 · 22 · 7 · 04.

I AM THE IMAGE, GORDON IS THE SUBSTANCE, BRITAIN IS THE WINNER

It was a delicate equation but very much the secret of our success to date. But time has changed, space has shifted, and a new reality obtains. Now in order to ensure future success there is a more compelling agenda: Gordon must die, Britain must be reforged in my image and the world will be a warmer place.

I AM BRITAIN

BRITAIN IS THE WORLD

THE WORLD SHALL
BE FREE

CHAPTER 22

Make Your Play

Alastair just called but I don't think I wish to speak to him at the moment. Politics, as I've said before, is all about performance, and performance is what I'm all about. I'm not certain where I acquired this unique capability, but I don't ever remember a time when I didn't have it. I have always possessed the absolute ability to believe whatever I say at the precise moment I am saying it, and I cannot stress enough how useful this has been to me in my political career.

E MAN WHO SAW **THE BIGGER PICTURE** — AFTER CHARLES ADDAMS —

Complete And Utter Sincere Conviction

I don't mean appear to believe: that would be the merest illusion, as practised by actors every single day and night of the year. I mean actually believe, with complete and utter sincere conviction. No other politician of the modern age has possessed this talent. Margaret Thatcher certainly didn't. She may have been considered a conviction politician, but she could never deliver and inspire conviction in the way I've always been able to.

Perhaps this fundamental inflexibility was her tragedy. I've often thought of writing and composing a Grand Opera about her because I think her legacy deserves no less, certainly not some fatuous musical satire, but writing and composing isn't really my thing. I'd ask one of the theatrical knights, say Hare, or whatsisname, to write the libretto, but none of them will speak to me any more.

"That was a splendid sermon you gave about
the 'Foolish Virgins,' Vicar.   I'll never be one again!"

CHAPTER 23

Queen Lear

I conceive it as a sort of 'Queen Lear' with three sons instead of daughters. Major and Hague would be Goneril and Regan (or Roneril and Gegan, or perhaps Panteril and Eebagum) and Cordelia, well, that could be me. Maybe not. I seem to recall that she comes to a bad end. I know! Gordelia!! Stroke of genius!! They'd all die and it would be very, very sad, gutwrenching even, in fact I'm starting to weep just thinking about it. Oh God, I'm so sad! John Prescott could be the fool, though possibly it could be Iain Duncan Smith if anybody could remember who he was, wandering off into the night with his unfortunate, swivel-eyed, blind mistress, both as mad as fish.

It's a Royal Washout!

A NOT IGNOBLE AMBITION...

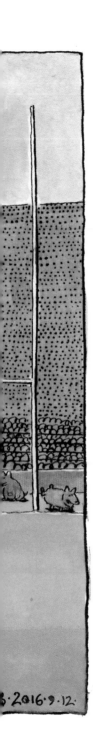

Limp Yet Massive

Imagine Gordelia, dead as a dodo, in his mad mother's arms, limp yet massive, his dead weight crushing her poor mad lap. The more I think about it the more appropriate it seems, because the thing that's always got to me is that I'm always the one who's been identified as the Thatcherite and it's just so unfair. Gordon is the real Thatcherite. Dry as dust with the most vicious, unyielding hatred for all things socialist, and every bit as inflexible as his mentor/mother figure.

CHAPTER 24

This Silly Game

This silly game he's played all these years, pretending to be the closet pinko while Muggins here carries the can for his crimes. Well, fuck the Welsh, fuck the Scots and fuck that for a game of soldiers! Gordelia, you are going to die most inauspiciously with your entire economic legacy in ruins and a laughing stock! Nothing will have come of nothing at the end of the day. Not that it's your legacy, it's my legacy, at least I'm the one it's pinned on. So unfair. So unfucking fair.

CHAPTER 25

Learn Your Lessons

- Never apologise, never explain.
- Do not get caught.
- If you are found out, do not confess.
- If you are caught confessing, redefine.

145

146

Stupendous Wealth

But it doesn't matter any more because, as I explained in rather more detail than I think I should have done, I am bound for a fourth landslide, as well as stupendous wealth derived from this programme for a Vision for a New You which the British people are going to buy in their millions, and if they don't I'll send Reid around to kick their heads in. It will be printed on recycled order papers and its carbon footprint will be so slight as to be undetectable. It will be fully illustrated and printed in full colour, but only using inks that have not been tested on seals or polar bears.

Time to Revise, Review, Reveal

I am
The Way,
The Truth,
The Life,
The Leader

CHAPTER 26

Successful Centre Ground Politics

Eat your heart out, future boy Digital Dave Cameron, whoever you are, wherever you are, even if it's the middle of next fucking week! And even you could follow my step-by-step guide to find out how successful centre ground politics are really done. It would certainly do you no harm and might actually pay dividends. Certainly a lot cheaper than cocaine and it won't make you sneeze or twitch.

CHAPTER 27

Get Out Of The Bathroom

Must go now. Cherie's knocking on the bathroom door. I fear it may be time for another MSB. Oh God! I think I've had enough. I don't really want another MSB. These days they seem to invoke awful fits of depression and that can't be right.

CHAPTER 28

The British People

I know! I can get onto the ledge through that small window and if I wade through the pigeon droppings I should be able to get up onto the roof. Then I can fly away. It's either that or be shot by an over-enthusiastic police marksman. There must be an easier way to make a living. Of course! There's always this book. I'll be able to retire on the proceeds. Won't have to worry my head about the British people anymore, God fuck 'em…

STABLE AND ORDERLY TRANSITION

Mind you, there won't be a book if I drop this fucking Dictaphone. It's all in there, you see. Oh shi…

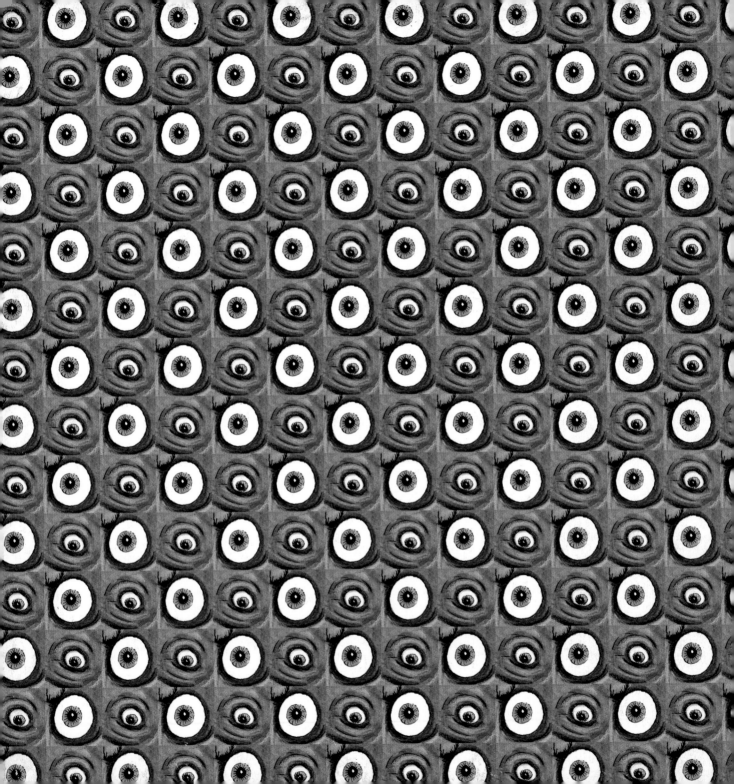